Bandwagon

Barry Maybury

OXFORD UNIVERSITY PRESS

Oxford University Press, Walton Street, Oxford OX2 6DP

OXFORD LONDON GLASGOW
NEW YORK TORONTO MELBOURNE WELLINGTON
IBADAN NAIROBI DAR ES SALAAM LUSAKA CAPE TOWN
KUALA LUMPUR SINGAPORE JAKARTA HONG KONG TOKYO
DELHI BOMBAY CALCUTTA MADRAS KARACHI

© Oxford University Press 1974

First published 1974
Reprinted 1977

By the same author:
Wordscapes, Thoughtshapes, Bandstand (Oxford University
Press)—companion collections of prose and verse
Creative Writing for Juniors (B. T. Batsford Ltd, London)

Filmset in Baskerville by
BAS Printers Limited, Wallop, Hampshire,
and printed in Great Britain at
the University Press, Oxford by
Vivian Ridler, Printer to the University

Contents

Some of the long passages are in a smaller type and are not illustrated. These are intended to be read aloud by the teacher.

Saturdays I put on my boots to go wading
down the River Pinn
singing songs like: Olly Jonathan Curly and Carrot
past garden trees, the backs of shops, building sites
scaffolds and timber, park-keepers' huts
the disused railway line and the new estate
the garage junk heap, twenty foot high in greasy
   springs
unstuffed car-seats, boxes in thousands
light bulbs, rubber stamps and an old typewriter,
through the woods where the woodpeckers used to be
and there are rapids and bogs and sand-flats,
you have to watch for hidden jaws in the mud
or beaver dams and Amazon settlements;
you can see into the back of the telephone exchange
to a million wires on the walls
and an all-red telephone
and there's Grolly's Grotto:
the tunnel under the library under the cleaners
under the bicycle sheds and the newspaper stand.
In the middle it smells black,
you can't see either end
the walls are wet and the water's deeper
where Thatcher fell in and under
and screamed for hours so it echoed and echoed
but we couldn't see him—
all we could hear was him splashing and thrashing
hitting the walls with his boots

us holding on to the mucky bricks
bumping into each other's arms
or shouting and shushing until it went quiet
and still in the dark. And then we ran.
Or swam. And fought. It was miles.
Rushed into the light covered in slime
looking at each other with eyes big and silly:
Where's Thatcher?
No one said we'd left him. Just us goggling—
waiting for a splosh or scud
It was raining where we stood
goggling in the light under the library where it was
    warm
not knowing that Thatcher was crawling out the other
    end.

MICHAEL ROSEN

Lovers lie around in it
Broken glass is found in it
Grass
I like that stuff

Tuna fish get trapped in it
Legs come wrapped in it
Nylon
I like that stuff

Eskimos and tramps chew it
Madame Tussaud gave status to it
Wax
I like that stuff

Elephants get sprayed with it
Scotch is made with it
Water
I like that stuff

Clergy are dumbfounded by it
Bones are surrounded by it
Flesh
I like that stuff

Harps are strung with it
Mattresses are sprung with it
Wire
I like that stuff

Carpenters make cots of it
Undertakers use lots of it
Wood
I like that stuff

Cigarettes are lit by it
Pensioners get happy when they sit by it
Fire
I like that stuff

Dankworth's alto is made of it, most of it,
Scoobdedoo is composed of it
Plastic
I like that stuff

Man made fibres and raw materials
Old rolled gold and breakfast cereals
Platinum linoleum
I like that stuff

Skin on my hands
Hair on my head
Toenails on my feet
And linen on my bed

Well I like that stuff
Yes I like that stuff
The earth
Is made of earth
And I like that stuff.

ADRIAN MITCHELL

My hands have been
                    working,
Working very hard,
Now they are hot,
Hot and clammy,
Their colour is pink and black.
Blotches of Black Ink.
They have been working
                    all day long.
Scrubbing teeth, washing faces
Eating Breakfast, Writing ~
What could I do
Without my hands?
Practically Nothing.

Pamela Spratt, 12

My dad's thumb

My dad's thumb
can stick pins in wood
without flinching—
it can crush family-size matchboxes
in one stroke
and lever off jam-jar lids without piercing
at the pierce here sign.

If it wanted
it could be a bath-plug
or a paint-scraper
a keyhole cover or a tap-tightener

It's already a great nutcracker
and if it dressed up
it could easily pass
as a broad bean or a big toe.

In actual fact, it's quite simply
the world's fastest envelope burster.

MICHAEL ROSEN

When the wind is strong,
The earth seems like someone's kite.
But as it is still high noon,
Men notice that night is already there.

The wind uses no words,
But only frets as it swirls about.
I think of the winds on other stars,
Whether they could be friends together.

On the earth, there is night, there is day.
Between them, what are the stars doing?
Silent, spreading. How do they endure?

In the daylight, the blue sky tells lies.
While the night mutters the truth, we are asleep.
And in the morning, we all say we dreamed.

TANIKAWA SHUNTARŌ

The sea at night

The sea splashes against
The shingle,
And the lighthouse lamps
Blink far and wide.
Tugs are tooting
In the fog,
Trawlers are trawling
Getting fish.
Dredgers are dredging
Sand from the sea,
Dark and gloomy.
The oyster bed is quiet
All over the sea
Little fish glide slowly,
Crabs are slowly
Sending bubbles
Through the night.

KEVIN, aged 7

At one moment, the bomb site had been a dark, bare area with a few shadowy figures lugging heavy objects, and then—as the match tickled up the paraffin, fire leapt out. In a moment the whole place was a wild inferno of crackling flames, jumping squibs, shooting rockets, bouncing bangers and whizzers. Dozens of demonic figures yelled and ran and leapt about, for in a few seconds the children had multiplied into hundreds.

Up, up, shot the flames, sending great sprays and showers of sparks into the night. All the old chairs, full of worm, beetle, and dry horse hair, caught like tinder and made a glowing core to the fire. Whizzers and bangers were now going off all over the place, exploding like jumping jacks in the very middle of the crowd, and starting yells of dismay and small fights. Screaming girls ran away and were pursued. All the windows in the houses around the bomb site had shot up, and their inhabitants were yelling protests and complaints, but not one of the children listened. Some of the adults saw the fun of the fire, but the duller ones, who were only greedy for their rights as citizens, rang up the police, the fire brigade, the Vicar or anyone else they fancied.

ELIZABETH STUCLEY

Morning

Birds whistle for it's a start of a new day,
The hustle and bustle of feet are heard by the window.
Rays of light shine through curtains.
Darkness turns to light, stillness to movement.
Morning is full of life.
Milk bottles jingle, papers rustle through the door.
Car horns honk, engines roar and brakes screech.
Water gurgles down the drain.
The sun bursts through the clouds,
Flowers open and animals hunt for their food.
Babies cry, voices shout,
Doors shut and cars start up their engines.
Weary eyes open,
People wearily get out of bed.
Smells fill the room,
Feet run, shuffle and stamp along the street.
Milkmen park their milk floats
Bakers park their vans.
Dogs bark, cats wail and birds sing.
Morning is here again.

CLARE, aged 9

You are sitting there
  Waiting,
Waiting, waiting for time to come.
Just sitting there, sitting there,
  Wondering.
Then time is coming, coming, coming,
It's coming
  Closer, closer, closer, closer,
Until it is suddenly right on top of you,
On top of you, on top of you.
Then it is gone
  Gone
Gone into the bewildering past where days,
  months, years
Hover in space
Without fear, without fail.
Time you see can never stop, stop, stop.
Time is the common factor that goes on
And on
And on
And on.
Tick tock tick tock.

ROBERT HUBBARD, aged 10

Greatly shining,
The Autumn moon floats in the thin sky;
And the fish-ponds shake their backs and flash
    their dragon scales
As she passes over them.

AMY LOWELL

Millionaires, presidents—even kings
Can't get along without everyday things.

Were you president, king or millionaire,
You'd use a comb to comb your hair.

If you wished to be clean—and you would, I hope—
You'd take a bath with water and soap.

And you'd have to eat—if you wanted to eat—
Bread and vegetables, fish and meat;

While your drink for breakfast would probably be
Milk or chocolate, coffee or tea.

You'd have to wear—you could hardly refuse—
Under clothes, outer clothes, stockings and shoes.

If you wished to make a reminding note,
You'd take a pencil out of your coat;

And you couldn't sign a letter, I think,
With anything better than pen and ink.

If you wanted to read, you'd be sure to look
At newspaper, magazine, or book;

And if it happened that you were ill,
You'd down some oil or choke on a pill.

If you have a cold I can only suppose
You'd use a handkerchief for your nose.

When you wanted to rest your weary head,
Like other folks, you'd hop into bed.

Millionaires, presidents—even kings
Can't get along without everyday things.

JEAN AYER

Flies

Everywhere there are
Rotten, sickening, terrifying flies.

I get into bed to have a rest;
Well, I tried my best.

For there all around were a
Million
Gillion
Quartetzillion
Disgusting, annoying,
Awaking, destroying
Flies,
Flying around, over my cupboard and in my hair.

I itch, I twitch,
But can't get them off.
I scratch, I kill,
But can't get them off.

I go to my bath,
I drown them off, but not all.

I disinfect them;
I get my frog to eat them.

Sickening, horrifying, disgusting,
Those hairy, sucking, sucking plague-bringers.

DAVID DANIELS, aged 9

Ranjit and the tiger

Ranjit walked from his village to the edge of the jungle. Then he saw something that made his heart jump. A tiger!

He ran as fast as his legs would carry him. He looked behind and *WHAM*! Down he fell.

His foot was tangled in the creeper. He looked round but where was the tiger? Why didn't the tiger chase him? He looked hard. The tiger was still there—Ranjit could see him.

Perhaps the tiger was hurt. Perhaps he had his foot caught in a creeper as well.

It took Ranjit a long time but he got his foot loose at last and he ran for all he was worth. Then he slowed down. What about the tiger? What would happen to him? He would starve to death. Or the hunters would come and shoot him.

Ranjit felt bad about the tiger now. He stopped. He turned round. He started to walk back.

The tiger was still there, looking at him. The tiger didn't look very fierce. He looked sad. Ranjit went closer. He knelt down and put out his hand towards the tiger's head. The tiger didn't move. Then Ranjit saw that the tiger's foot was caught in a tangle of creepers. It was bleeding. Ranjit moved his hand closer and the tiger moved his head a little. But he didn't growl, nor did he snarl. He let Ranjit undo the creeper from his foot. It was hard work and took a long time. The foot was bleeding a lot and the tiger began to lick it.

Ranjit stood up and slowly walked away. There was no more he could do. He hoped the tiger wouldn't leap on him when his back was turned.

After a while he looked round. The tiger was following him. He waited. The tiger came up to him. He was limping. The tiger rubbed his nose against Ranjit's side. He was being friendly.

Ranjit put out his hand and stroked the tiger's thick golden
hair.

'You'd better go back,' he said and walked away. But the tiger
still followed him.

Ranjit thought about it. If he went home with the tiger every-
body would be terrified. Somebody might try to shoot him.
So he turned round and went with the tiger back to the jungle.

The tiger quietly padded along at his side. He let Ranjit stroke
his head and fondle his ears. He didn't mind. Sometimes he would
rub his nose on Ranjit's side. Ranjit was very pleased to have
such a great friend. After all, the tiger was king of the animals in
this jungle.

After a while Ranjit began to think the tiger was leading him.

Perhaps he's taking me to his lair, thought Ranjit. Well, I
might as well go with him, now I've come this far. So on he
went.

Ranjit saw many creatures in the jungle, such as the cobra,
wild pig, and monkeys chattering away in the trees. They soon
scuttled away when they saw he was with the tiger.

Presently they came to a place where there was a huge rock
covered all over with creepers and roots from the trees that grew
out high above it. Ranjit followed the tiger down a track. It
wasn't easy. They scrambled over some rocks and then at last
there was the entrance to a cave.

As Ranjit climbed up behind the tiger he saw that there were
cubs in the cave. Coming out quickly was a tigress. Ranjit was
afraid for he knew that female tigers were very fierce, especially
when they had cubs. But when they all saw Ranjit's tiger they were
friendly. They came up to Ranjit and rubbed against him. He
was very proud. He was probably the only boy in the world to have
a family of tigers for his friends.

Ranjit was happy staying with the tigers. He played with the cubs who kept running into each other and falling over, and he explored the cave which went deep into the mountain and once he had a ride on the tigress's back. He had to hold on very tight because she moved so fast through the forest.

But he couldn't stay there for ever. He had to get back home. His mother would worry about him if he was out after dark.

'Goodbye, tigers,' he said. He knew they could not understand him but he felt he had to say something to them. He stroked each one of them in turn and patted their heads which they seemed to like. Then he waved goodbye and set off for home.

But he didn't feel so safe in the jungle as he did when he was with the tiger. There were strange moving shapes of animals. He knew that there were creatures lurking in the dark places of the forest. He hurried on. Sometimes he saw the swift movement of the cobras in the bushes and he ran, cutting his arms on sharp branches. He was beginning to wish he had stayed with the tigers. But now he had to keep on to his village. He knew the way for he was used to the jungle. His father had taken him into it many times when he was hunting. But always his father had a fine gun. Now he was alone with no weapons.

He heard a sound behind him and, turning, he tripped and fell. He was soon on his feet again but when he looked up there in a tree just above him was the long and powerful body of a leopard. It was staring straight at Ranjit and its mouth was curled up in an ugly snarl. Ranjit knew that it was getting ready to leap. If he ran it would soon catch up with him. If he stayed there it would leap out onto him. What could he do? If only he could call his tiger friends.

It was his only chance. He put his hands to his mouth and shouted in a loud voice: 'GOODBYE TIGERS.' He hoped the tigers would hear him and recognise his voice.

The leopard was surprised by the call and stopped for a minute.

He didn't know what to make of the call.

Ranjit stood his ground and stared at the leopard. The leopard stared at him. The leopard wasn't sure what to do. He crouched ready to spring and with a snarl on his face, but he didn't spring. And then Ranjit heard it.

The sound of the tiger. So his friend had heard him.

The tiger came bounding up, huge and fierce. It leapt up at the leopard who drew back spitting and snarling. The tiger lashed out with his terrible claws. The leopard shrank back and then he turned tail and bounded away into another tree and into the jungle.

Ranjit turned to his friend.

'Thank you, tiger.' he said. 'I did you a good turn, and now you have done one for me.'

He said goodbye to the tiger once more and set out for home. He didn't have far to go now. Before he stepped out of the forest he turned and looked back. The tiger was still standing there in the path staring after him. He waved and hurried on.

When he got back he was very tempted to tell all about the tiger, but he didn't. He thought they would say he was making it up, or more likely they would want to go and hunt the tiger with the big gun.

So Ranjit kept quiet about it and never told a soul.

Only sometimes when he had nothing to do he would wander into the jungle and call to his friends, or perhaps stroll up to their cave.

They never forgot him. And he knew that whatever dangers there were in the jungle, he at least was safe from them when his friends the tigers were about.

PADDY KINSALE

They waited patiently for what seemed a very long time, stamping in the snow to keep their feet warm. At last they heard the sound of slow shuffling footsteps approaching the door from the inside. It seemed, as the Mole remarked to the Rat, like some one walking in carpet slippers that were too large for him and down at heel; which was intelligent of Mole, because that was exactly what it was.

There was the noise of a bolt shot back, and the door opened a few inches, enough to show a long snout and a pair of sleepy blinking eyes.

'Now, the *very* next time this happens,' said a gruff and suspicious voice, 'I shall be exceedingly angry. Who is it *this* time, disturbing people on such a night? Speak up!'

'O, Badger,' cried the Rat, 'let us in, please. It's me, Rat, and my friend Mole, and we've lost our way in the snow.'

'What Ratty, my dear little man!' exclaimed the Badger, in quite a different voice. 'Come along in, both of you, at once. Why, you must be perished. Well I never! Lost in the snow! And in the Wild Wood, too, and at this time of night! But come in with you.'

The two animals tumbled over each other in their eagerness to get inside, and heard the door shut behind them with great joy and relief.

The Badger, who wore a long dressing-gown, and whose slippers were indeed very down-at-heel, carried a flat candlestick in his paw and had probably been on his way to bed when their summons sounded. He looked kindly down on them and patted both their heads. 'This is not the sort of night for small animals to be out,' he said paternally. 'I'm afraid you've been up to some of your pranks again, Ratty. But come along; come into the kitchen.

There's a first-rate fire there, and supper and everything.'

He shuffled on in front of them, carrying the light, and they followed him, nudging each other in an anticipating sort of way, down a long, gloomy, and, to tell the truth, decidedly shabby passage, into a sort of central hall, out of which they could dimly see other long tunnel-like passages branching, passages mysterious and without apparent end. But there were doors in the hall as well—stout oaken comfortable-looking doors. One of these the Badger flung open, and at once they found themselves in all the glow and warmth of a large fire-lit kitchen.

The floor was well-worn red brick, and on the wide hearth burnt a fire of logs, between two attractive chimney corners tucked away in the wall, well out of any suspicion of draught. A couple of high-backed settles, facing each other on either side of the fire, gave further sitting accommodation for the sociably disposed. In the middle of the room stood a long table of plain boards placed on trestles, with benches down each side. At one end of it, where an arm-chair stood pushed back, were spread the remains of the Badger's plain but ample supper. Rows of spotless plates winked from the shelves of the dresser at the far end of the room, and from the rafters overhead hung hams, bundles of dried herbs, nets of onions, and baskets of eggs. It seemed a place where heroes could fitly feast after victory, where weary harvesters could line up in scores along the table and keep their Harvest Home with mirth and song, or where two or three friends of simple tastes could sit about as they pleased and eat and smoke and talk in comfort and contentment. The ruddy brick floor smiled up at the smoky ceiling; the oaken settles, shiny with long wear, exchanged cheerful glances with each other; plates on the dresser grinned at pots on the shelf, and the merry firelight flickered and played over everything without distinction.

The kindly Badger thrust them down on a settle to toast themselves at the fire, and bade them remove their wet coats and boots. Then he fetched them dressing-gowns and slippers, and himself bathed the Mole's shin with warm water and mended the cut with sticking-plaster till the whole thing was just as good as new, if not better. In the embracing light and warmth, warm and dry at last, with weary legs propped up in front of them, and a suggestive clink of plates being arranged on the table behind, it seemed to the storm-driven animals, now in safe anchorage, that the cold and trackless Wild Wood just left outside was miles and miles away, and all that they had suffered in it a half-forgotten dream.

KENNETH GRAHAME

Barney has fallen into a pit where he has met a strange prehistoric character he calls 'Stig'.

He'd never seen anything like the collection of bits and pieces, odds and ends, bric-à-brac and old brock, that this Stig creature had lying about his den. There were stones and bones, fossils and bottles, skins and tins, stacks of sticks and hanks of string. There were motor-car tyres and hats from old scarecrows, nuts and bolts and bobbles from brass bedsteads. There was a coal scuttle full of dead electric light bulbs and a basin with rusty screws and nails in it. There was a pile of bracken and newspapers that looked as if it were used for a bed. The place looked as if it had never been given a tidy-up.

'I wish I lived here,' said Barney.

Stig seemed to understand that Barney was approving of his home and his face lit up. He took on the air of a householder showing a visitor round his property, and began pointing out some of the things he seemed particularly proud of.

First, the plumbing. Where the water dripped through a crack in the roof of the cave he had wedged the mud-guard of a bicycle. The water ran along this, through the tube of a vacuum-cleaner, and into a big can with writing on it. By the side of this was a plastic football carefully cut in half, and Stig dipped up some water and offered it to Barney. Barney had swallowed a mouthful before he made out the writing on the can: it said WEEDKILLER. However, the water only tasted of rust and rubber.

It was dark in the back of the cave. Stig went to the front where the ashes of a fire were smoking faintly, blew on them, picked up a book that lay beside his bed, tore out a page and rolled it up, lit it at the fire, and carried it to a lamp set in a niche in the wall. As it flared up Barney could see it was in fact an old teapot, filled with some kind of oil, and with a bootlace hanging out of it for a wick.

In the light of the lamp Stig went to the very back of the cave and began to thump the wall and point, and explain something in his strange grunting language. Barney did not understand a word but he recognized the tone of voice—like when grown-ups go on about: 'I'm thinking of tearing this down, and building on here, and having this done up . . .' Stig had been digging into the wall, enlarging his cave. There was a bit of an old bed he had been using as a pick, and a baby's bath full of loose chalk to be carried away.

Barney made the interested sort of noises you are supposed to make when people tell you they are going to put up plastic wall-paper with pictures of mouse-traps on it, but Stig reached up to a bunch of turnips hanging from a poker stuck in the wall. He handed Barney a turnip, took one for himself, and began to eat it. Barney sat down on a bundle of old magazines done up with string and munched the turnip. The turnip at least was fresh, and it tasted better to him than the cream of spinach he'd hidden under his spoon at dinner time.

Barney looked at Stig. Funny person to find living next door to you, he thought. Stig did not seem much bigger than himself, but he looked very strong and his hands looked cleverer than his face. But how old was he? Ten? Twenty? A hundred? A thousand?

'You been here long?' asked Barney.

Stig grinned again. 'Long,' he said. 'Long, long, long.' But it sounded more like an echo, or a parrot copying somebody, than the answer to his question.

'I'm staying at my Grandmother's house,' said Barney. Stig

just looked at him. 'Oh well,' thought Barney, 'if he's not interested in talking I don't mind.' He stood up. 'I better go now,' he said. 'Thank you for having me. Can I have my knife back, please?'

Stig still looked blank.

'Knife,' said Barney, and made cutting movements with his hand. Stig picked up the sharp worked flint from the floor of the cave and gave it to Barney.

'Oo, can I have that!' exclaimed Barney. 'Thank you!'

He looked at the stone, hard and shiny, almost like a diamond and much more useful. Then he put it in his pocket, said good-bye again, and went out of the low door of the shelter.

It was getting late in the autumn evening, and it was already dark and gloomy in the pit. Barney knew there was a way out right at the other end of the pit, and by going a long way round he could get back to the house. There were rustlings in dry leaves and muffled sounds from the middle of bramble patches, but somehow Barney found he didn't mind. He felt the hard stone in his pocket and thought of Stig in his den under the cliff. You weren't likely to find anything stranger than Stig wherever you looked. And, well, Stig was his friend.

CLIVE KING

Procure some strips of beef, and having cut them
into the smallest possible slices, proceed to cut them
still smaller, eight or perhaps nine times.

When the whole is thus minced, brush it up hastily
with a new clothes-brush, and stir round rapidly and
capriciously with a saltspoon or a soup-ladle.

Place the whole in a saucepan, and remove it to
a sunny place,—say the roof of the house if free from
sparrows or other birds,—and leave it there for about
a week.

At the end of that time add a little lavender,
some oil of almonds, and a few herring-bones; and then
cover the whole with 4 gallons of clarified
crumbobblious sauce, when it will be ready for use.

Cut it into the shape of ordinary cutlets, and
serve up in a clean tablecloth or dinner-napkin.

EDWARD LEAR

'I've eaten many strange and scrumptious dishes
    in my time,
Like jellied gnats and dandyprats and earwigs
    cooked in slime,
And mice with rice—they're really nice
When roasted in their prime.
(But don't forget to sprinkle them with just a pinch
    of grime.)

'I've eaten fresh mudburgers by the greatest cooks
    there are,
And scrambled dregs and stinkbugs's eggs and
    hornets stewed in tar,
And pails of snails and lizards' tails,
And beetles by the jar.
(A beetle is improved by just a splash of vinegar.)

'I often eat boiled slobbages. They're grand when
    served beside
Minced doodlebugs and curried slugs. And have
    you ever tried
Mosquitoes' toes and wampfish roes
Most delicately fried?
(The only trouble is they disagree with my inside.)

'I'm mad for crispy wasp-stings on a piece of
    buttered toast,

And pickled spines of porcupines. And then a
  gorgeous roast
Of dragon's flesh, well hung, not fresh—
It costs a pound at most,
(And comes to you in barrels if you order it by post.)

'I crave the tasty tentacles of octopi for tea
I like hot-dogs, I LOVE hot-frogs, and surely
  you'll agree
A plate of soil with engine oil's
A super recipe.
(I hardly need to mention that it's practically free.)

'For dinner on my birthday shall I tell you what I
  chose:
Hot noodles made from poodles on a slice of
  garden hose—
And a rather smelly jelly
Made of armadillo's toes.
(The jelly is delicious, but you have to hold your nose.)

'Now comes,' *the Centipede declared*, 'the burden
  of my speech:
These foods are rare beyond compare—some are
  right out of reach;
But there's no doubt I'd go without
A million plates of each
For one small mite,
One tiny bite
Of this FANTASTIC PEACH!'   ROALD DAHL

Making pancakes when my mother was out

It was all her own fault really; she said she wasn't going to make any pancakes this year because she hadn't got time. So when Sally and Bill came round I said it was all right for them, *they* could have pancakes for *their* tea but we couldn't have any for ours, Ruthie and me. Sally said, 'Let's make 'em for her. I know how to do it.' 'Yeah,' said Bill. 'Save her the trouble. I know how to make pancakes as well. You get some baking flour and mix it up with a lot of eggs and sugar. I've seen my mom do it hundreds of times.' 'I thought you had to have lard in it,' I said. 'No,' said Bill, 'that's when you're making roly-polys—I think.' 'Bet you don't know at all,' I said. 'Stop it, Ruthie,' I said, because she was trying to make a pancake of her own out of a piece of horrible old bread she had got hold of out of the waste bin. She always goes scrabbling about in our waste bin when your back is turned. She's only two so I suppose she doesn't know any better. Trouble is, she eats it if you don't watch her. Anyway, I thought it would be a good idea to make some pancakes for when mom came home. It would save her the trouble. So I agreed.

We got out a big dish and I climbed on a stool and reached the

I climbed on a stool..... .....reached the flour down... ...knocking the sugar over.....

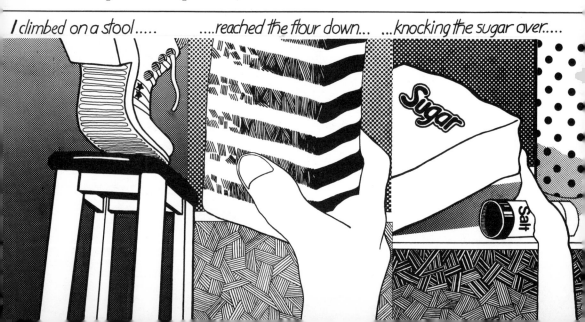

flour down from the cupboard, knocking the sugar over as I did it. That was the first accident. You know what sugar's like—it seems to get all over the place—in the bread and butter, all over the floor, and some of it was on Ruthie's head. She didn't mind. She was licking it up as it trickled down her face.

We put some flour in the dish and scraped the sugar into it off the table. There were a few bread crumbs as well but we didn't think it would matter very much because, as Bill said, bread was made from flour anyway. Then Sally broke some eggs into it and dropped one on the floor. I was just going for the floor-cloth to get it up when Ruthie went and stood in it. 'Naughty girl!' I said, and she started to cry and backed away, bumping into Bill who was just taking the top off a bottle of milk so that it jerked his hand and the milk went everywhere, most of it all over my back, because I was kneeling down trying to get the egg up. 'I've got half an eggshell in this,' Sally said. 'I can't get it out.' She was trying to fish it out with a pencil, and the more she fished the further it got stuck in the goo. 'Oh, leave it,' Bill said. 'We can pull it out when the things are cooking in the frying-pan.' So Sally started to stir it up but it didn't look right at all. 'It's the milk that needs putting in it,' Bill said and poured this pint of milk

.....Sally broke some eggs into the bowl and dropped one.....

as Sally had just let go of the pencil, so that she had to stick her hand in it to get the pencil out. 'Ugh!' she said. 'Horrible and sticky!' waving her hand about in the air and milk and blobs of egg and stuff were flying about. Bill started laughing and leaned back—right on the two eggs that were left on the table. 'Ughowgh!' he said when he saw yellow sticky egg all over his sleeve. 'Ughowgh,' said Ruthie, imitating him and watching the egg drip off the table into her hand. 'Come out, you lot,' I said. 'Mom'll go mad.' I managed to wipe most of the egg with a tea towel which I hid behind the sink. Sally had found a spoon at last and was stirring up the sickly-looking mixture. We all peered at it with wrinkled noses. 'Think it'll be all right?' I said. 'Looks a bit scrobbly,' Bill said. It was all sort of sloppy with big gobbets of eggy flour floating about in it. 'Funny,' Sally said. 'Doesn't look like that when my mom does it. Perhaps we should put some salt in it.' So I got this plastic salt container which has a little cap at the top to stop the salt from rushing out all at once, but there must have been something the matter with it because as I tipped it up the top came off and about half a pound of salt wooshed into the mixture. The plastic cap just sank like a stone in a pond. We all looked at it. 'Won't taste very nice now, will it?' said Bill.

....the milk went everywhere....

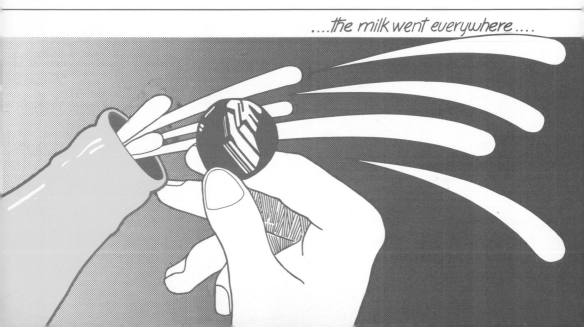

'Well, put some sugar in it so the salt won't be noticed,' Sally said. Bill then emptied the rest of the sugar into the mixture and Sally went on stirring. We forgot all about the cap. 'I think it's ready now,' Sally said. We got the frying-pan on the stove and turned up the heat. Then Sally poured in some of the stuff and flattened the lumps down a bit, but instead of just cooking it started to let out squeaks and a terrible smoke, and within seconds the kitchen was so full you could hardly see anything. I was trying to open the window and accidentally knocked the handle of the frying-pan so that it pitched out the evil-looking mess of a pancake onto the floor. Some of it went on Bill's shoe and some stuck to the stove and began to go black and send out more smoke. We were so busy trying to get it up, opening the door, turning off the stove and waving the smoke out with newspapers and the lid of the bread bin, that nobody noticed that Ruthie had got the basin in a corner and was slopping out what was left of the mixture in great handfuls into *my* wellingtons.

That was when mom came in. I try to forget what happened after that, but a big black gloom came down on the scene. We all decided later that cooking wasn't really in our line.

PADDY KINSALE

....*that was when mom came in...* .....*end.*

'The whole lift is made of thick clear glass!' Mr Wonka
declared. 'Walls, doors, ceiling, floor, everything is
made of glass so that you can see out!'

'But there's nothing to see,' said Mike Teavee.

'Choose a button!' said Mr Wonka. 'The two
children may press one button each. So take your pick!
Hurry up! In every room, something delicious and
wonderful is being made.'

Quickly, Charlie started reading some of the labels
alongside the buttons.

○ *The Rock Candy mine—10 000 feet deep*, it said on one.
Cockernut-ice skating rinks, it said on another.

Then . . .

○ *Strawberry-juice water pistols*

○ *Toffee-apple trees for planting out in your garden
—all sizes*

○ *Exploding Sweets for your enemies*

○ *Luminous Lollies for eating in bed at night*

○ *Mint Jujubes for the boy next door
—they'll give him green teeth for a month*

○ *Cavity-filling Caramels
—no more dentists*

○ *Stickjaw for talkative parents*

○ *Wriggle-sweets that wriggle delightfully in your tummy
after swallowing*

○   *Invisible Chocolate Bars for eating in class*

○   *Sugar-coated Pencils for sucking*

○   *Fizzy Lemonade swimming pools*

○   *Magic Hand-fudge*
    —when you hold it in your hand, you taste it in your mouth

○   *Rainbow Drops*
    —suck them find you can spit in six different colours

'Come on, come on!' cried Mr Wonka. 'We can't wait all day!'

ROALD DAHL

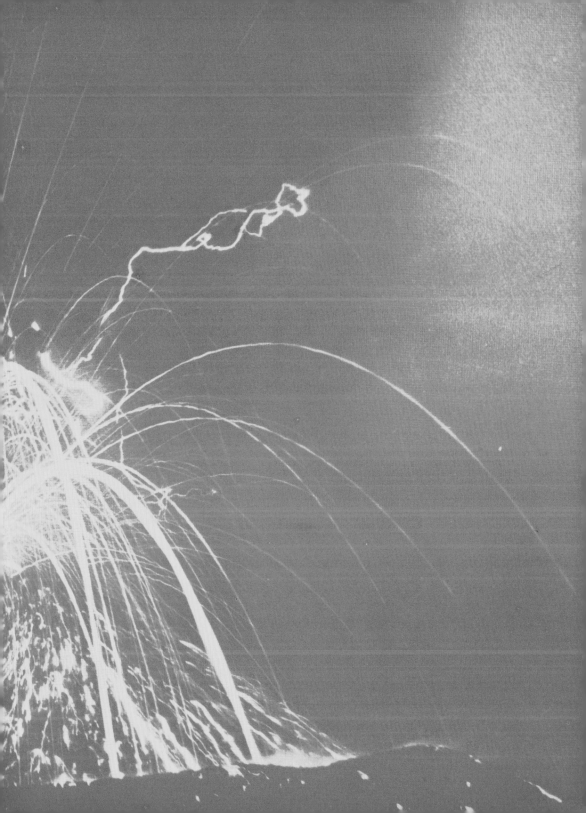

There's a very funny insect that you do not often spy,
And it isn't quite a spider, and it isn't quite a fly;
It is something like a beetle, and a little like a bee,
But nothing like a woolly grub that climbs upon a tree.
Its name is quite a hard one, but you'll learn it soon, I hope.
So, try:
    Tri-
        Tri-anti-wonti-
            Triantiwontigongolope.

It lives on weeds and wattle-gum, and has a funny face;
Its appetite is hearty, and its manners a disgrace.
When first you come upon it, it will give you quite a scare,
But when you look for it again you find it isn't there.
And unless you call it softly it will stay away and mope.
So, try:
    Tri-
        Tri-anti-wonti-
            Triantiwontigongolope.

It trembles if you tickle it or tread upon its toes;
It is not an early riser, but it has a snubbish nose.
If you sneer at it, or scold it, it will scuttle off in shame,
But it purrs and purrs quite proudly if you call it by its name,
And offer it some sandwiches of sealing-wax and soap.
So, try:
> Tri-
> > Tri-anti-wonti-
> > > Triantiwontigongolope.

But of course you haven't seen it; and I truthfully confess
That I haven't seen it either, and I don't know its address.
For there isn't such an insect, though there really might have
  been
If the trees and grass were purple, and the sky was bottle-green.
It's just a little joke of mine, which you'll forgive, I hope.
Oh, try!
> Try!
> > Tri-anti-wonti-
> > > Triantiwontigongolope.

C. J. Dennis

```
        ow!
        wow!
      bowwow!
      !bowwow
     w!bowwo
     ow!boww
    wow!bow
   wwow!bo
  owwow!b
 bowwow!
      wow!
      ow!
```

EDWIN MORGAN

KARL FLETCHER,
aged 11

CAT.   CAT.

A SMALL
THING
NICE SOFT
FLUFFY
FUR
SOME LONG
THIN WISKERS.
FROM ITS WET
SMALL NOSE, TWO
CUDDLY EYES AND
A MOUTH WITH SMALL
SHARP TEETH. FOUR
SMALL SKINNY
LEGS WITH
FOUR FL-
ABBY PAWS THE BOTTOM

IMAGINE THE WORLD IF WHEELS HAD BEEN SQUARE

'Twas midnight in the schoolroom
And every desk was shut,
When suddenly from the alphabet
Was heard a loud 'Tut-tut!'

Said A to B, 'I don't like C;
His manners are a lack.
For all I ever see of C
Is a semi-circular back!'

'I disagree,' said D to B,
'I've never found C so.
From where *I* stand, he seems to be
An uncompleted *O*.'

C was vexed, 'I'm much perplexed,
You criticise my shape.
I'm made like that, to help spell Cat
And Cow and Cool and Cape.'

'He's right,' said E; said F, 'Whoopee!'
Said G, ''Ip, 'ip, 'ooray!'
'You're dropping me,' roared H to G.
'Don't do it please I pray!'

'Out of my way,' LL said to K.
'I'll make poor I look ILL.'
To stop this stunt, J stood in front,
And presto! ILL was JILL.

'U know,' said V, 'that W
Is twice the age of me,
For as a Roman V is five
I'm half as young as he.'

X and Y yawned sleepily,
'Look at the time!' they said.
'Let's all get off to beddy byes.'
They did, then, 'Z-z-z.'

SPIKE MILLIGAN

There was once a king who had a proclamation made throughout his kingdom that whoever told him the biggest lie would receive an apple of pure gold. All sorts of people came to him and told him lies, but the king always shook his head and said:

'That's all very well, but it could be true.'

One day a young man arrived, holding a barrel in his hand.

He said to the king:

'Oh mighty monarch, I have come for the gold sovereigns.'

'What gold sovereigns?' asked the king.

'The barrel of gold sovereigns you borrowed from me last week!'

'I certainly never borrowed a barrel of gold sovereigns from you. That's a lie!'

'If it's a lie, then give me the golden apple!'

The king stopped short:

'Wait a moment, you're quite right! I've just remembered!'

'All the better, my liege, then give me the barrel of gold sovereigns!'

The king realised that he had been outwitted, and that was how the young man won the golden apple.

VLADISLAV STANOVSKY and JAN VLADISLAV
(trans. Jean Layton)

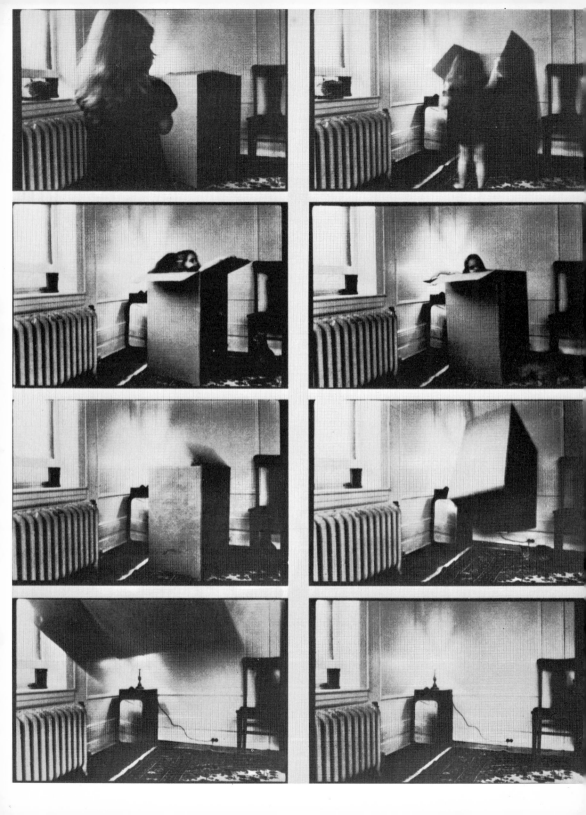

An accident happened to my brother Jim
When somebody threw a tomato at him—
Tomatoes are juicy and don't hurt the skin,
But this one was specially packed in a tin.

ANON.

My aunt she died a month ago,
And left me all her riches,
A feather bed and a wooden leg,
And a pair of calico breeches,
A coffee-pot without a spout,
A mug without a handle,
A baccy box without a lid,
And half a farthing candle.

ANON.

If all the world were paper,
And all the sea were ink,
If all the trees were bread and cheese,
What should we have to drink?

ANON.

Sam, Sam, the butcher man,
Washed his face in a frying pan,
Combed his hair with a wagon wheel,
And died with a toothache in his heel.

ANON.

A pin has a head, but has no hair;
A clock has a face, but no mouth there;
Needles have eyes, but they cannot see;
A fly has a trunk without lock or key;
A timepiece may lose, but cannot win;
A corn-field dimples without a chin;
A hill has no leg, but it has a foot;
A wine-glass a stem, but not a root;
Rivers run, though they have no feet;
A saw has teeth, but it does not eat;
Ash-trees have keys, yet never a lock;
And baby crows, without being a cock.

CHRISTINA ROSSETTI

On Nevsky Bridge a Russian stood
Chewing his beard for lack of food.
Said he, 'It's tough this stuff to eat
But a darn sight better than shredded wheat!'

ANON.

There was a young girl in the choir
Whose voice arose higher and higher,
    Till one Sunday night
    It rose quite out of sight,
And they found it next day on the spire.

ANON.

The fantastic machine

Jim Tinker had a meccano set one Christmas. He never made much with it and it was put away in a cupboard. And then it got mixed up with a lot of old junk his uncle Sid gave to his Dad. Of course it got left down the shed.

One day in the holidays when he had nobody to play with Jim went down to the shed and was messing about with all this junk. He made a thing like a fire engine, didn't like it, and took it to pieces again. He made an aeroplane, didn't like it and took that to pieces. He wanted to make something special. Something you could sit on, fly about in, cruise under water in. He wanted a special machine.

His mother called him for his dinner. All through dinner he was thinking about the machine. He began to imagine it. He couldn't wait to get his dinner over and be down that shed.

When he finished eating he rushed down to the shed and began work. He got a plank of wood, screwed down some pieces of meccano and some other pieces from uncle Sid's junk. He made a pair of swept-back wings from some sheets of aluminium. He fixed on a coil of wire and made some levers out of an old broom handle.

All afternoon he was working. The machine grew bigger and bigger. It became more complicated as he put more and more things on it until at last it was finished. He stood back and looked at it.

It was a fantastic machine. He could sit on it, move the lever back and forward, press a button with his feet to make it go faster or slower. All it needed was an engine. But where would he get an engine? He thought about it. Up in the attic was an old gramophone. If he could use that . . . ?

He ran to ask his mother. He hadn't been any trouble all

afternoon so she didn't mind helping him to get the gramophone from the attic. It was very dusty and part of it was missing.

'All right,' she said, 'You can have it. It's broken anyway, so it's no good for anything.'

Off he went back to the shed with his engine. It was a bit of a struggle because the engine was quite heavy. He drilled a couple of holes in the front of the plank and bolted the engine down onto it. Then he made a propeller out of aluminium and bolted that onto the back end. Then he took a piece of old washing line and fixed it round the turntable of the gramophone and round the wheel onto which his propeller was fixed. He pulled it tight and tied it in a reef knot. Then he had a trial run. He wound up the gramophone. It worked the drive belt he'd made from the washing line and turned the propeller.

The great moment had come. He wound up the engine as far as it would go and then sat on the machine. He could just reach the starting lever with his foot. He closed his eyes, felt for the lever with his foot and turned it. There was a rattling and a vibrating, a rumbling and a clanking of the things in the shed. The machine rose a few inches off the floor of the shed and Jim opened his eyes just in time to see himself floating out through the door and up over the garden. Now that the machine was in the air the engine ran smoothly and silently.

He flew over the houses and high above the factory, over the canal, over the seven fields, rising higher and higher until he could no longer make out cars on the roads or cows in the fields. He could have gone on flying all day but he realised that if he wasn't careful he would fall out. He had forgotten to make a safety belt, so he turned the machine round and flew lower and lower until he recognized his own street and his own garden. It was one of those warm sunny afternoons when people are dozing in chairs if they're not at work, or bending over weeding the garden, so nobody had seen Jim. And nobody had heard him because his engine was silent.

At first he landed the machine on the lawn, but then he found he could control it and fly it just above the ground so he gently drove it into the shed and settled it on the floor. The engine just wound down as he got off.

He soon made the safety belt. But all the while he was doing that he was thinking of other things he could add to the machine. It was a bit windy up there so he needed a covering. And if he was to go under water his cockpit would have to be waterproof. He got some perspex and made a cabin which he sealed with rubber from an old bike inner tubing.

At last the machine was ready for its second flight. But just one thing more. He fixed a strap round his foot which looped onto the handle, so that he could wind up the engine when it ran down.

Once more he set off, out of the shed and high over the estate, over the fields until he came to the lake shimmering beneath him. Now we'll see what she's like diving, he thought to himself. He banked over to the left and went into a steep dive, heading down towards the lake. He made a final check that the cabin was screwed down tight and plunged into the water. There had been a great rushing of air when he dived but now all had gone quiet under the water. When the bubbles cleared he could see for quite a long way and a few fishes came to join him.

It was very peaceful under the water and Jim tried a few turns and a few dives. He didn't go to the bottom of the lake because it was dark down there and he had no light. That was the next thing he must do—fix a torch-light for diving underwater. As he got closer to the side of the lake he could see that there were plenty of places to explore, but he could do nothing without a light.

He turned back to the middle of the lake and got ready to rise up again out of the water. He began moving at a fair speed and when he thought it was the right time he broke the surface of the water and streamed up into the air above the lake.

It was nice being out in the air again so he decided to go for a little flight. He glided around the lake a couple of times just to make sure he could find his way home and then he gave the engine a few extra winds and headed out over the water.

He seemed to rise quicker and faster, and soon he could see mountains in the distance. He was heading towards Wales. He looked at the roads winding their way over passes through woods and across bleak moors. And then he saw a magnificent mountain. It was Cader Idris. He turned towards it and soared up over the little lake to the summit of the great mountain.

It was such a fine day, and there was nobody about so Jim thought he would walk about a bit on the top of the mountain. He brought the machine gently to rest on the rocks and stepped out of the cockpit. He could see for miles—the sea in the distance, other mountains rising up. But when he looked down below him he could see some walkers heading towards the summit. He didn't much like the idea of anybody seeing his machine. It was his secret. So he got back into the cockpit and wound up the machine. He released the catch but nothing happened. He tried again. Nothing. He got out. The engine wouldn't turn, and it was very hot. What could be the matter with it? Perhaps it needed oil. He remembered his father was always putting oil into their old car. But where could he get oil on the top of Cader Idris? He was stuck. The voices of the walkers were getting closer. Well, they'd just have to see him.

Soon they were coming up to the machine. It was a young man and his girl.

'How on earth did this get here?' said the young man.

'I flew it,' said Jim. 'But I've run out of oil.'

The young man and the girl began to laugh.

'It isn't funny,' said Jim crossly. 'I can't get back.'

The young man became serious and had a look at Jim's engine.

'Mm..,' he muttered. 'It does look as if you need oil. I don't know where you'd get oil up here.'

'I've got some sun-tan oil, if that's any good,' said the girl. She took a plastic bottle out of her rucksack. The young man put a few drops into the engine. Jim turned the engine a few times and it began to work.

'Thanks,' he said. 'Don't tell anybody, will you?'

'Oh, no,' laughed the young man and then looked in amazement as Jim climbed into his machine and slowly rose into the air. He looked down and saw them standing there astonished. He waved a couple of times and headed home.

It wasn't easy to find his way back but he managed it. He flew in low over the allotments so that nobody would see him and was soon drifting gently into the shed. The engine had just stopped when Jim heard his mother calling.

She came down the garden and looked in at the door.

'Where have you been, Jim? I've been looking all over for you. Your tea'll be dried up in the oven. I thought you were playing in here. Where were you?'

'I was just—,' began Jim.

'Well, come on, and don't go off like that again without telling anybody,' said his mother, walking away down the path.

Before following her Jim oiled the engine and wiped the dust from the perspex cockpit. It was the best thing he'd ever made, and it was only the first of many adventures he had with it.

BARRY MAYBURY

Faster and faster flew the seagulls, skimming across the sky at a tremendous pace, with the peach trailing out behind them. Cloud after cloud went by on either side, all of them ghostly white in the moonlight, and several more times during the night the travellers caught glimpses of Cloud-Men moving around on the tops of these clouds, working their sinister magic upon the world below.

Once they passed a snow machine in operation, with the Cloud-Men turning the handle and a blizzard of snowflakes blowing out of the great funnel above. They saw the huge drums that were used for making thunder, and the Cloud-Men beating them furiously with long hammers. They saw the frost factories and the wind producers and the places where cyclones and tornadoes were manufactured and sent spinning down toward the Earth, and once, deep in the hollow of a large billowy cloud, they spotted something that could only have been a Cloud-Men's city. There were caves everywhere running into the cloud, and at the entrances to the caves the Cloud-Men's wives were crouching over little stoves with frying-pans in their hands, frying snowballs for their husbands' suppers. And hundreds of Cloud-Men's children were frisking about all over the place and shrieking with laughter and sliding down the billows of the cloud on toboggans.

An hour later, just before dawn, the travellers heard a soft *whooshing* noise above their heads and they glanced up and saw an immense grey batlike creature swooping down toward them out of the dark. It circled round and round the peach, flapping its great wings slowly in the moonlight and staring at the travellers. Then it uttered a series of long deep melancholy cries and flew off again into the night.

'Oh, I do wish the morning would come!' Miss Spider said, shivering all over.

'It won't be long now,' James answered. 'Look, it's getting lighter over there already.'

They all sat in silence watching the sun as it came up slowly over the rim of the horizon for a new day.

ROALD DAHL

Lament on losing a kite

Aue! Aue!
My kite-string's bust!
My kite's gone off,
It's lost in space,
It's gone for good!

    All right, kite:
    Fly on to visit.
    Visit here and visit there—
    Old Wind has got you now.

    And where have you gone—
    To the home of the stars?
    Where are you clinging—
    To the breast of the sky?

Aue! My kite's flown off,
It's tangled with the far side of the sky.
Its head is hanging down
All drooping in the wind.

That string snapped in my hands,
Snapped under my foot—

Useless end of string!
Now I'm starting to cry—
I sound like a startled duck.

It is *lost!*

Maori Chant

Three children—Jacko, Dave and Dave's sister, Ruthie—have been given remarkable powers by visitors from outer space. They can become invisible and also fly, though not at the same time.

They went to the rear of the park, to a place where Jacko knew it was easy to get through the railings. Before they did this though they took the precaution of first becoming invisible, just in case somebody should happen to come along and catch them.

Once inside the park they made for the bandstand which was surrounded by trees, and screened from the council houses on one side. Jacko was the first to become visible and go into the air, and Dave watched in excitement as his companion rose above the bandstand higher and higher, before he himself, holding Ruthie's hand, climbed gently into the air. It was a wonderful sensation to watch the bushes grow smaller, then the bandstand drop away below so that they could see its roof. A few sparrows took to the air in a terrified flurry of feathers and disappeared to the shelter of the trees. A crow squawked and nearly fell out of the air. A squirrel that had suddenly appeared from nowhere scampered back for dear life into an elm as the three children soared higher and higher. They could see above the tree-tops now and across the park to the football pitch on which they some-times played from school.

'Hey,' said Dave. 'Look! We s'll have to come down a bit.' They turned in the air and looked round. Behind them, where they had floated above the huge elm trees and the roofs of the houses, could be seen windows and gardens beyond.

'They'll be able to see us,' giggled Jacko, drifting away. The others followed him until they were out of sight of the houses.

'Hey, look at this,' said Jacko, gambolling in the air, turning somersaults and standing on his head. Dave and Ruth tried it and, finding it easy, began rolling about and spiralling like seagulls. Occasionally Dave would just stop dead, braking hard, after running fast through the air, and simply stand bolt-upright. It made him chuckle to himself and finally roar with laughter; simply standing there in the air seemed comical.

They could glide like birds, lie down or roll over; they could run about backwards and forwards, or up and down; they could stand on each other's shoulders in three tiers, or just swim about like flying fish, and once Dave bounced himself high into the air and came down again like a ball. Ruthie wanted to do it but Dave insisted on holding her hand, and, with a great leap, they went up and up like a pair of rockets at a tremendous speed. Looking down, they could see the park, becoming smaller, almost disappearing beneath them; the houses and the roads, the cars, the church and the flats all moving away from them at such a rate that soon the houses were no more than little dots and the children were high in the clouds. They were both gulping air, staggering about, finding it hard to breathe.

'Better go down,' shouted Dave, because of the noise of the air as it rushed past them. 'In case we get lost,' feeling suddenly that they might not be able to find their way back straight down to the park.

They swivelled round a moment and hovered before plunging down again very fast into the maze of houses and roads and buildings, but aiming for the green patch they both hoped was the park. They began to slow up as they came closer, recognizing the pool and the trees.

'Wow!' yelled Dave. 'Better not—do—that again,' he was gasping. 'Somebody's bound—to see us.' They were both lolling about dizzily.

'You could go zoom,' said Jacko, looking up into the sky. 'You went up so quick it was like a ball. I'm havin' a go.' And before Dave could remonstrate, Jacko was shooting up into the air and within seconds was no more than a 'tiny spot. Dave and Ruthie entertained themselves doing cartwheels and handstands about ten feet above the ground, until Jacko came down again. He was hurtling so fast Dave thought he would crash into the ground, but he seemed to brake about three feet up and skid in the air.

'Eh, kid, it's great!' he exclaimed. 'Beats swimmin' any day.'

Ruthie was turning over and over very slowly like a wheel, when something caught her eye.

'Look!' she called. They all stopped stock-still in the air and looked in the direction in which she was pointing. There, about fifty yards away, was a park-keeper with his mouth wide open and a look of sheer astonishment on his face.

'Yoiks!' Dave yelled. 'Quick! Down to the ground and disappear.' They all three landed and dematerialised. The amazed park-keeper ran like a frenzied cat with a ghost on his tail, scattering sparrows, as fast as his fat legs would carry him, into the trees and howling wildly for help.

'Better clear off,' Jacko said to his invisible companions, sensing they were close by. And all three of them were soon out through the railings and off home, becoming visible when they went down an entry and out the other end.

'Bloody done it now!' said Dave.

'Aw, he won't tell,' said Jacko. 'Who'd believe him that he'd seen three kids flyin' about in the air and then disappearing when they landed?'

'He'd think he'd been seeing things,' Ruthie said, giggling at her memory of the way the park-keeper ran into the trees. But they all resolved on the way home not to try it again unless they were sure nobody was about.

BARRY MAYBURY

Good fortune did not always go with me and on one occasion, though I fought valiantly, I was taken captive by the Turks and sold as a slave to the Sultan. The work I was given to do was not arduous and I began to enjoy it. Each day I would drive out the Sultan's bees to their pasture grounds and each day in the evening I would bring them back to their hives. One day, however, as I was bringing them home I discovered that one of them was missing and going back to find her I came upon two bears who had set upon the unfortunate bee (for as you know bears are very fond of honey) and were about to tear her to pieces so that they could enjoy the precious nectar she carried. I had no suitable weapon about me so I took out the small axe given to all gardeners by the Sultan and threw it at the bears, intending to frighten them away and set the bee at liberty, but by an unlucky pitch of the arm the axe flew upwards and continued in that direction until it reached the moon. What was I to do? How could I possibly fetch it down again? And then I remembered that Turkey-beans grow very quickly and reach an amazing height. Naturally, I planted one straight away and stood to watch it grow, which it did until it reached up to the moon, actually fastening itself to one of the moon's horns. All I had to do now was to climb up to the moon which I did very quickly. The only difficulty I met was in finding my axe because of the brightness of the light everywhere. Eventually, however, I came across it in a heap of straw. Now, I was all ready to return, but consider my surprise when I discovered that the heat from the sun had shrivelled up my beanstalk so that it was of no use at all for my descent. What could I do? I looked around and saw the straw. Of course, I would make a rope! I set to work weaving the straw and soon had used it all up in making my rope. One end of it I tied round one of the moon's horns and the other I threw down to the earth below and slid down it until I reached the end. Here I held on tightly with my left hand while with the hatchet in my right hand I cut the piece of useless rope above me and tied it to the lower end which I was holding on to. This allowed me to clamber down further of course. And so by repeated cutting and tying on the used up rope I was able to climb down further towards the earth. Unfortunately, the constant cutting of the rope began to shorten it and at last I ran out of rope altogether when I was at least five miles above the earth. I fell to the ground with such tremendous force that I found myself stunned and in a hole nine fathoms deep at least which was made by the weight of my body falling from such a great height. When I became conscious again I could see that the problem was now to get out of the deep hole in the ground, but since my nails were very long and tough I managed to dig steps in the sides of the hole and climb out of it again. Peace was restored soon afterwards with the Turks so I was set free, and, of course, continued my adventures.

BARON MUNCHAUSEN

Witches

A star-white sky
Trees rustling as the wind lulls them to sleep
Shadowy creatures slinking through the grass
Clouds sailing,
Tattered and torn
Ragged and ripped.
Suddenly
In the sky
Soaring
   Zooming
      Diving about
         Flittering
Swooping into the air
Come witches
Cloaks ragged and torn
Streaming behind.
Cackling, laughing
Fading into the darkness.

LINDEN, aged 10

Spooky girls

In the dark night of London
Two spooky girls go by
They run like fairies
They run like winds
All the way along

Then people look from windows
Give a little scream
It's spooky girls
It's spooky girls
Get your girl and boy to bed

As the sun goes up
The spooky girls go
But when it's down
We see the spooky girls
Run like the wind
In the dark dark roads

ALISON ANN HUNT, aged 9

The cat

Within that porch, across the way,
  I see two naked eyes this night;
Two eyes that neither shut nor blink,
  Searching my face with a green light.

But cats to me are strange, so strange—
  I cannot sleep if one is near;
And though I'm sure I see those eyes
  I'm not so sure a body's there!

W. H. DAVIES

The Wendigo,
The Wendigo!
Its eyes are ice and indigo!
Its blood is rank and yellowish!
Its voice is hoarse and bellowish!
Its tentacles are slithery,
And scummy,
Slimy,
Leathery!
Its lips are hungry blubbery,
And smacky,
Sucky,
Rubbery!
The Wendigo,
The Wendigo!
I saw it just a friend ago!
Last night it lurked in Canada;
Tonight, on your veranada!
As you are lolling hammockwise
It contemplates you stomachwise.
You loll,
It contemplates,
It lollops.
The rest is merely gulps and gollops.

OGDEN NASH

The doze

Through Dangly Woods the aimless Doze
A-dripping and a-dribbling goes.
His company no beast enjoys.
He makes a sort of hopeless noise
Between a snuffle and a snort.
His hair is neither long nor short;
His tail gets caught on briars and bushes,
As through the undergrowth he pushes.
His ears are big, but not much use.
He lives on blackberries and juice
And anything that he can get.
His feet are clumsy, wide and wet,
Slip-slopping through the bog and heather
All in the wild and weepy weather.
His young are many, and maltreat him;
But only hungry creatures eat him.
He pokes about in mossy holes,
Disturbing sleepless mice and moles,
And what he wants he never knows—
The damp, despised, and aimless Doze.

JAMES REEVES

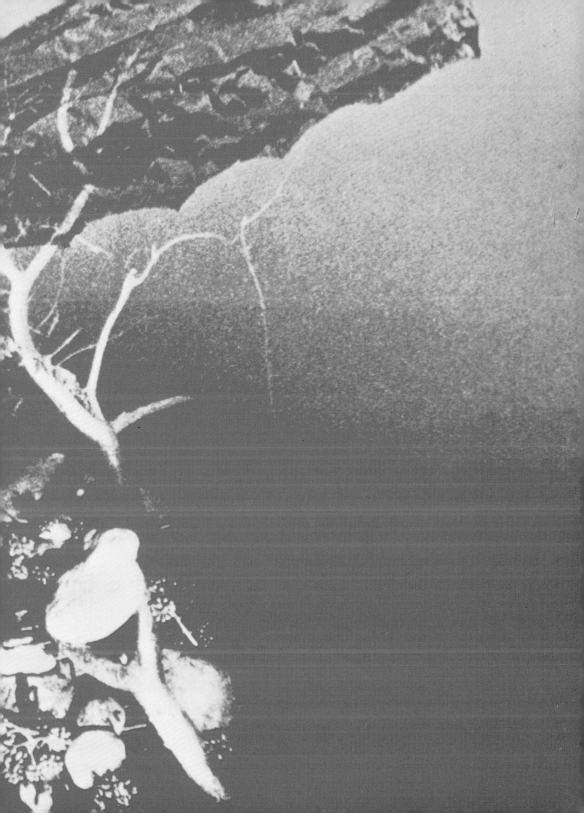

Out of the dark wood
Comes a twisted evil creature
Covered by scales of rust.
He is thousands of years old
An iron creature corrugated all over and flaky.
He crawled up sliding and groaning
Clanking and tinkling as he went
Tearing through the undergrowth.
He rose up out of the dark black sea
Long, long ago in the age of reptiles.
He was an outcast made of iron
Had to leave the sea
And crawl with his ugly legs
On land. He has been hiding here for
Many generations.

PETER, aged 11

Acknowledgements

The author gratefully acknowledges permission to reproduce extracts from the following copyright works:
Antony Alpers: 'Lament on Losing a Kite' from *Legends of the South Sea*. Reprinted by permission of John Murray (Publishers) Ltd. **Jean Ayer:** 'Everyday Things' from *Come Follow Me* (Evans Brothers Ltd.) Reprinted by permission of E. Gould Chalker. **Roald Dahl:** 'Centipede's Song' and the extract from *James and the Giant Peach* illus. J. Schindelman (copyright © 1961 by Roald Dahl) and 'Wonka's Chocolate Factory' from *Charlie and the Chocolate Factory* illus. N. E. Burkert (copyright © 1964 by Roald Dahl). Reprinted by permission of George Allen & Unwin Ltd and Alfred A. Knopf, Inc. **W. H. Davies:** 'The Cat' from *Collected Poems of W. H. Davies*. Reprinted by permission of Jonathan Cape Ltd. **C. J. Dennis:** 'The Triantiwontigongolope' from *A Book for Kids*. Reprinted by permission of Angus and Robertson (U.K.) Ltd. **James C. Gibson** and **Raymond Wilson** (editors): 'Time' by Robert Hubbard (aged 10) from *Rhyme and Rhythm*. Reprinted by permission of the author and Macmillan, London and Basingstoke. **Kenneth Grahame:** *The Wind in the Willows* (© 1908 Scribner's). Reprinted by permission of Methuen & Co. Ltd. and the Bodleian Library and Charles Scribner's Sons. **Clive King:** *Stig of the Dump*. Reprinted by permission of Hamish Hamilton Ltd. **Richard Lewis** (ed.): 'Witches' by Linden (aged 10) from *Miracles*, copyright © 1966 by Richard Lewis. Reprinted by permission of Penguin Books Ltd. and Simon and Schuster Inc. **Amy Lowell:** 'Wind and Silver' from *The Complete Poetical Works of Amy Lowell*. Reprinted by permission of Houghton Mifflin Company. **Barry Maybury** (ed.): 'Out of the dark wood' by Peter (aged 11) from *Creative Writing for Juniors*. Reprinted by permission of B. T. Batsford Ltd. **Spike Milligan:** 'The ABC' from *The Little Pot Boiler*. Reprinted by permission of Dennis Dobson Publishers. **Adrian Mitchell:** 'I like that stuff' from *Poems*. Reprinted by permission of Jonathan Cape Ltd. **Edwin Morgan:** 'Dogs round a Tree' from *Starryveldt* (Gomringer Press, Frauenfeld). Reprinted by permission of the author. **Ogden Nash:** 'The Wendigo'. Reprinted by permission of J. M. Dent and Sons Ltd. and Little, Brown & Co. **James Reeves:** 'The Doze' from *Prefabulous Animals*. Reprinted by permission of William Heinemann Ltd. **Tanikawa Shuntarō:** 'When the Wind is Strong' from *The Penguin Book of Japanese Verse* translated by Geoffrey Bownas and Anthony Thwaite. © Geoffrey Bownas and Anthony Thwaite 1964. Reprinted by permission of Penguin Books Ltd. **Vladislav Stanovsky** and **Jean Vladislav:** 'The Golden Apple' trans. Jean Layton from *Fairy Tale Tree* (Golden Pleasure Books). Reprinted by permission of Hamlyn Publishing Group Ltd. **Elizabeth Stucley:** *Magnolia Buildings*. Reprinted by permission of the Bodley Head.

The author would also like to thank the following for permission to reprint their poems and prose pieces:
Birmingham Education Department for 'The Sea at Night' by Kevin (aged 7) and 'Morning' by Clare (aged 9) from *Birmingham Children Write*; The Daily Mirror Children's Literary Competition for 'Spooky Girls' by Alison Hunt (aged 9); David Daniels (aged 9) for 'Flies'; Karl Fletcher (aged 11) for 'The Cat'; Paddy Kinsale for 'Ranjit and the Tiger' and 'Making Pancakes'; Michael Rosen for 'Saturdays I put on my boots to go wading' and 'My Dad's Thumb' and Pamela Spratt (aged 12) for 'My hands have been working'.

CHILDREN'S WORK